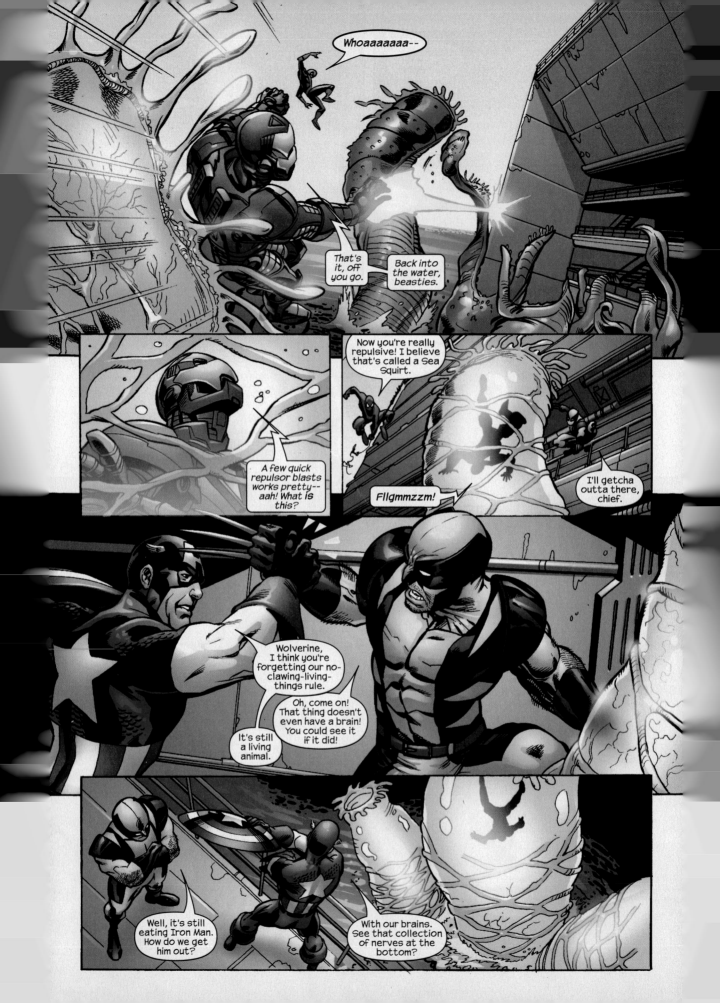

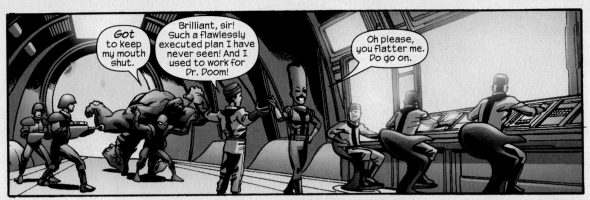

Got to keep my mouth shut.

Brilliant, sir! Such a flawlessly executed plan I have never seen! And I used to work for Dr. Doom!

Oh please, you flatter me. Do go on.

Mutating the sea life at the research center was the first master stroke. Instantly a threat that would require The Avengers help, yet look like an accident of science!

Well, it was really the cellular work that was tricky. Where was I when I thought of that?

Then having the squid knock the Hulk into the Man O' War, where you knew the megadoses of toxin would sting him unconscious!

Oh, it's so easy to mind-control simple animals--that reminds me, pump the seawater out of Hulk's lungs, will you?

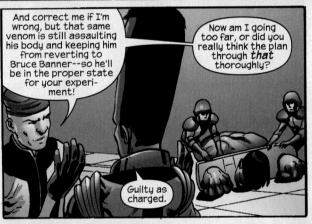

And correct me if I'm wrong, but that same venom is still assaulting his body and keeping him from reverting to Bruce Banner--so he'll be in the proper state for your experiment!

Now am I going too far, or did you really think the plan through *that* thoroughly?

Guilty as charged.

I suppose I'm going to have to listen to the rest of this master plan?

It's your lucky day. First, my men have to secure those hands--you're not webbing up my beautiful submarine!

Let me guess: the real goal of all this is so you can make wearing top hats mandatory, isn't it?

Stop him, imbeciles!

How did he know about the top hats?

Hah! Now Hulk make Bighead sorry!

Wait, Hulk! Listen!

Every time things start to go right for you...just when you finally feel happy and calm... *who* always takes your place? Who always lets you exist *only* when things are going bad?

That... weak little *Banner*.

That's right! Doctor Banner.

Poor Emil here would love to be human again for a time.

Yeah. That'd be great.

Yet he can't. However, I could lift these curses from both of you.

My latest creation here could transfer your condition to him. The Abomination could become an ordinary human again, at will.

And you...you would always be yourself. You'd never have to become Banner again. *Ever.*

GET MARVEL Adventures

DELIVERED TO YOUR DOOR!

To subscribe online go to: marvel.com/subscribe

GREAT FOR KIDS!

SUBSCRIBE AND SAVE!

☐ Subscribe to MARVEL ADVENTURES: SPIDER-MAN today and **SAVE 44%** off the newsstand price!*
You'll get 12 issues of fun and adventure for just $19.97!

☐ Get 24 issues for only $37.94! **SAVE 47%**

181MSD

_____
Child's Name (please print)

_____
Address   Apt.

_____
City   State   Zip

_____
Parent's Signature

_____
Parent's E-Mail

☐ Payment enclosed   ☐ Please bill me   *vs. newsstand price of $35.88 for 12 issues.

Send an additional $10 for Canadian and $12 for foreign orders prepaid in U.S. Funds. Allow 6-8 weeks for delivery.
TM & © 2007 Marvel Characters, Inc. All rights reserved.

GREAT FOR KIDS!

SUBSCRIBE AND SAVE!

☐ Subscribe to X-MEN: FIRST CLASS today and **SAVE 44%** off the newsstand price!*
You'll get 12 issues of fun and adventure for just $19.97!

☐ Get 24 issues for only $37.94! **SAVE 47%***

181XFD

_____
Child's Name (please print)

_____
Address   Apt.

_____
City   State   Zip

_____
Parent's Signature

_____
Parent's E-Mail

☐ Payment enclosed   ☐ Please bill me   *vs. newsstand price of $35.88 for 12 issues.

Send an additional $10 for Canadian and $12 for foreign orders prepaid in U.S. Funds. Allow 6-8 weeks for delivery.
TM & © 2007 Marvel Characters, Inc. All rights reserved.

GREAT FOR KIDS!

SUBSCRIBE AND SAVE!

☐ Subscribe to MARVEL ADVENTURES: AVENGERS today and **SAVE 44%** off the newsstand price!*
You'll get 12 issues of fun and adventure for just $19.97!

☐ Get 24 issues for only $37.94! **SAVE 47%***

181AVD

_____
Child's Name (please print)

_____
Address   Apt.

_____
City   State   Zip

_____
Parent's Signature

_____
Parent's E-Mail

☐ Payment enclosed   ☐ Please bill me   *vs. newsstand price of $35.88 for 12 issues.

Send an additional $10 for Canadian and $12 for foreign orders prepaid in U.S. Funds. Allow 6-8 weeks for delivery.
TM & © 2007 Marvel Characters, Inc. All rights reserved.

BUSINESS REPLY MAIL
FIRST-CLASS MAIL   PERMIT NO. 48   NEWBURGH NY

POSTAGE WILL BE PAID BY ADDRESSEE

MARVEL COMICS
PO BOX 110
NEWBURGH NY 12551-9923

BUSINESS REPLY MAIL
FIRST-CLASS MAIL   PERMIT NO. 48   NEWBURGH NY

POSTAGE WILL BE PAID BY ADDRESSEE

MARVEL COMICS
PO BOX 110
NEWBURGH NY 12551-9923

BUSINESS REPLY MAIL
FIRST-CLASS MAIL   PERMIT NO. 48   NEWBURGH NY

POSTAGE WILL BE PAID BY ADDRESSEE

MARVEL COMICS
PO BOX 110
NEWBURGH NY 12551-9923

To subscribe online go to: marvel.com/subscribe

GET MARVEL Adventures

DELIVERED TO YOUR DOOR!

The End

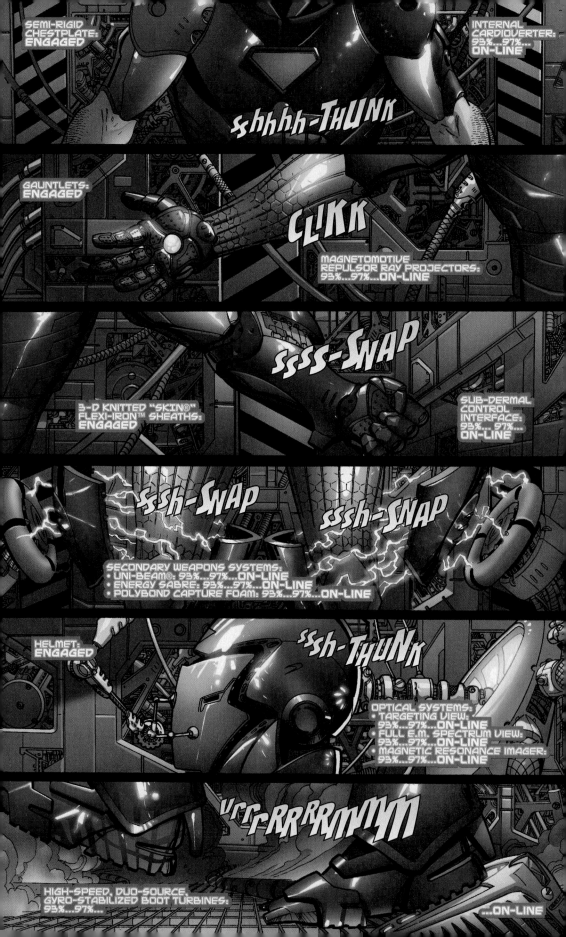

IRON MAN:
ENGAGED

IRON MAN:
ON-LINE

THE NEWS FLASH SAID ADVANCED IDEA MECHANICS HAS TARGETED THE FEDERAL RESERVE BANK OF NEW YORK.

THAT'S AT THIRTY-THREE LIBERTY STREET IN MANHATTAN. I'LL UPLOAD THE COORDINATES INTO YOUR G.P.S. NOW--

DON'T BOTHER, RHODEY...

HEART OF STEEL

Written by FRED VAN LENTE   Penciled by JAMES CORDEIRO   Inked by SCOTT KOBLISH
Colored by STUDIO F's MARTEGOD GRACIA   Lettered by BLAMBOT's NATE PIEKOS
Cover by MICHAEL GOLDEN   Assistant Editor – NATHAN COSBY   Editor – MARK PANICCIA
Editor in Chief – JOE QUESADA   Publisher – DAN BUCKLEY

"ADVANCED IDEA MECHANICS TERRORISTS HAVE TAKEN YOUR UNI-BEAM AND HOVER PLATFORMS...COMBINED THEM INTO SIEGE ENGINES THAT ARE LAYING WASTE TO MADRIPOOR EVEN AS WE SPEAK!

"OUR GOVERNMENT IS NEAR COLLAPSE-- ALL BECAUSE OF YOU AND YOUR MACHINES! AND NO ONE IN THE WEST SEEMS TO CARE!"

BOOO

BOOO

C'MON, GRANDPA, THE EXIT'S THIS WAY...

...FOR YOUR OWN HEALTH I SUGGEST YOU USE IT.

BITTER OLD FAILURE...TRYING TO RUIN STARKWORLD!

ANY WAY YOU CAN USE YOUR OLD SERVICE CONNECTIONS, RHODEY, FIND OUT IF THERE'S ANY TRUTH TO HIS RANTING?

THERE'S CALLS I CAN MAKE. BUT I'M SURE THE GEEZER'S JUST ANOTHER CRACKPOT, TONE.

WAIT-- AREN'T YOU GOING TO FINISH YOUR ADDRESS, BOSS?

NOT NOW, PEPPER-- I'M NOT IN THE MOOD.

DESPITE THE SOUR-- AND ABRUPT--END TO HIS KEYNOTE ADDRESS, TONY STARK MADE GOOD ON HIS PROMISE TO ATTEMPT TO CIRCLE THE GLOBE WITH POWERLESS FLIGHT.

NOT SINCE THE DAYS OF CHARLES LINDBERGH AND THE SPIRIT OF ST. LOUIS HAS AN AERONAUTICAL FEAT BEEN ANTICIPATED WITH SUCH EXCITEMENT...

EXCELLENT. THANK YOU, DOCTOR.

Ah, MR. STARK. **WELCOME.**

WE WERE AFRAID WE HAD LOST YOU.

AND **THAT** WOULD HAVE BEEN MOST **UNFORTUNATE.**

AS YOU ARE NOW--AND FOREVER--AN INVALUABLE ASSET...

...TO ADVANCED IDEA MECHANICS!

YOU MAY CALL ME THE... **SCIENTIST SUPREME.**

THEY'VE CERTAINLY PROVIDED US WITH EVERYTHING WE'D NEED TO FORGE AN *ARSENAL* UNLIKE ANYTHING THE WORLD HAS EVER *SEEN.*

WHAT MAKES THEM THINK WE WON'T JUST TURN THE WEAPONS WE MAKE ON *THEM* AND BUST OUR WAY *OUT* OF HERE?

FOR ONE THING, THEY ARE *WATCHING* US QUITE CLOSELY.

I AM QUITE SURE THIS ROOM IS *BUGGED* AS WELL.

AND THEY OUTNUMBER US A THOUSAND TO *TWO.* EVEN IF WE WERE ABLE TO ARM OURSELVES, WITHOUT ANY KIND OF PROTECTION WE'D BE CUT DOWN *INSTANTLY*--

YES...THAT ALL MAKES SENSE--

≶Unnnnnh≷

AND THIS...HEART CONDITION...IS NO *JOKE.*

AND LOOK AT THIS. THEY'VE EVEN DUMPED THE WRECKAGE OF THE OSPREY-1 IN HERE TO MOCK ME...FLAUNT THEIR POWER.

I SUPPOSE... A.I.M. IS *RIGHT.* WE HAVE NO OTHER *CHOICE.*

LET'S GET TO *WORK.*

SUPER HERO WORD SEARCH

KIDS: FIND THESE WORDS!

PETER PARKER

SPIDER-MAN

GIANT GIRL

IRON MAN

WOLVERINE

CAPTAIN AMERICA

STORM

HULK

TONY STARK

VENOM

```
P R X Q E F L A Q Y
E V Y G A J W G K L
T S P I D E R M A N
E N J A I E Q C B M
R T F N Y X H O V D
P K Z T F I D Z G E
A P I G R W G N M C
R W R I Q R B O W A
K E O R X K N Z U P
E V N L T E R B N T
R C M A V X B Y U A
M Y A H N E Z A P I
U C N B Q J R Y O N
B N F T Y R C I B A
H U L K W K G H N M
Q P Z B R M G T X E
J Y R S T O R M K R
B T W P C B F Y J I
C M Y N J X P G Z C
T O N Y S T A R K A
```

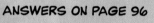

ANSWERS ON PAGE 96

THE REPORTS WE RECEIVED APPEAR TO BE **ACCURATE**, RHODEY...

...OUR STARK CHINA FACILITY, **THREE THOUSAND WORKERS** STRONG, LOOKS COMPLETELY **DESERTED!**

EVERYONE'S JUST...**VANISHED!**

ENTER THE DRAGON

WRITER - FRED VAN LENTE
PENCILER - JAMES CORDEIRO
INKER - SCOTT KOBLISH
COLORIST - STUDIO F'S MARTEGOD GRACIA
LETTERER - BLAMBOT'S NATE PIEKOS
COVER - MICHAEL GOLDEN
PRODUCTION - IRENE LEE
ASSISTANT EDITOR - NATHAN COSBY
EDITOR - MARK PANICCIA
EDITOR IN CHIEF - JOE QUESADA
PUBLISHER - DAN BUCKLEY

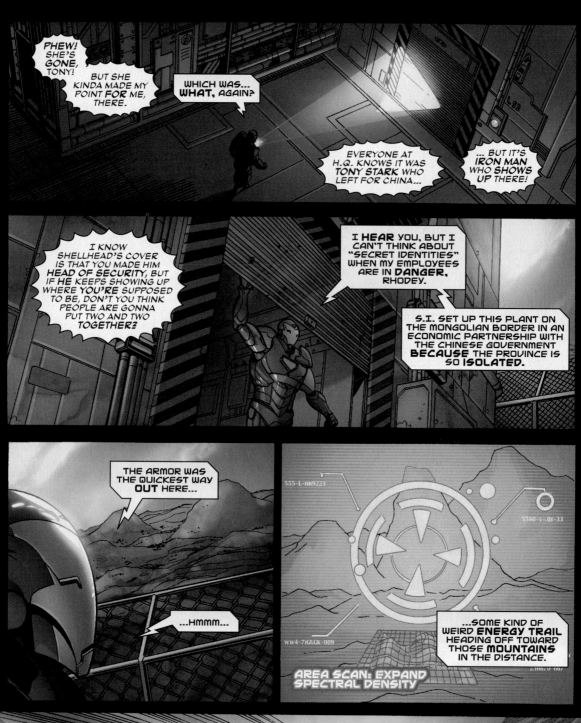

PHEW! SHE'S GONE, TONY!

BUT SHE KINDA MADE MY POINT FOR ME, THERE.

WHICH WAS... WHAT, AGAIN?

EVERYONE AT H.Q. KNOWS IT WAS TONY STARK WHO LEFT FOR CHINA...

... BUT IT'S IRON MAN WHO SHOWS UP THERE!

I KNOW SHELLHEAD'S COVER IS THAT YOU MADE HIM HEAD OF SECURITY, BUT IF HE KEEPS SHOWING UP WHERE YOU'RE SUPPOSED TO BE, DON'T YOU THINK PEOPLE ARE GONNA PUT TWO AND TWO TOGETHER?

I HEAR YOU, BUT I CAN'T THINK ABOUT "SECRET IDENTITIES" WHEN MY EMPLOYEES ARE IN DANGER, RHODEY.

S.I. SET UP THIS PLANT ON THE MONGOLIAN BORDER IN AN ECONOMIC PARTNERSHIP WITH THE CHINESE GOVERNMENT BECAUSE THE PROVINCE IS SO ISOLATED.

THE ARMOR WAS THE QUICKEST WAY OUT HERE...

...HMMM...

555-L-HH9223

5560-Y-.Qr-33

WW4-7TG6GK-009

...SOME KIND OF WEIRD ENERGY TRAIL HEADING OFF TOWARD THOSE MOUNTAINS IN THE DISTANCE.

AREA SCAN: EXPAND SPECTRAL DENSITY

SINCE THERE'S NO SIGN OF A STRUGGLE OR ANY OTHER CLUES AT THE PLANT ITSELF...

...IT'S THE ONLY LEAD WORTH FOLLOWING!

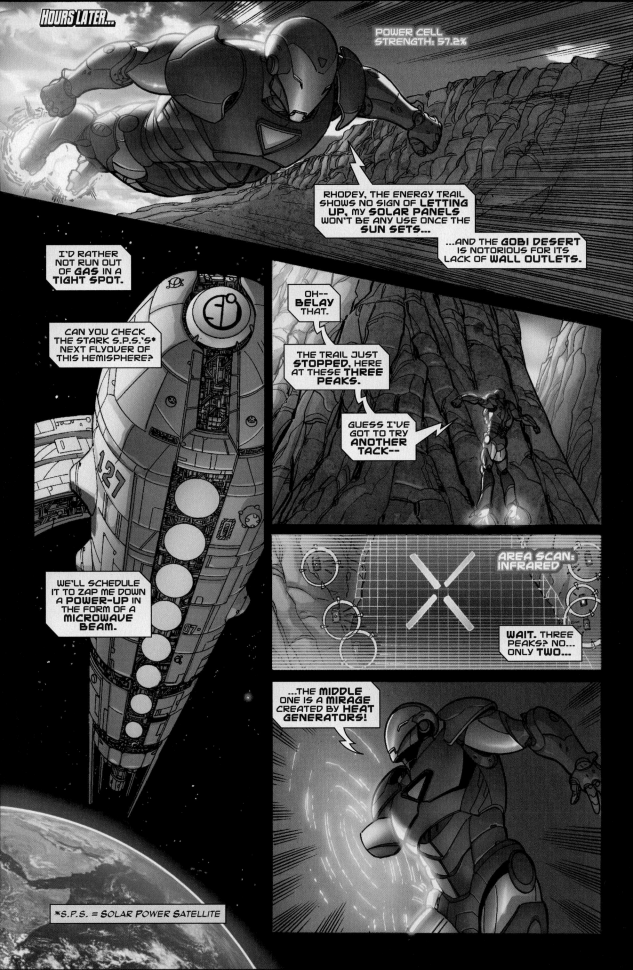

NON-LETHAL
DETERRENT:
ACTIVATED

SONAR:
ACTIVATED

TAKING:
EVASIVE
ACTION

AUTOPILOT:
TARGET COORDINATES:
PUBLIC AREA: 100 KM
SOUTHEAST

‹FASCINATING.›

‹SHALL WE GIVE *PURSUIT*, O GREAT *KHAN*?›

‹NO. IT IS TOO *LATE* FOR IRON MAN, OR TONY STARK, OR ANYONE *ELSE* TO *STOP* ME.›

PURSUIT?
NEGATIVE

LOCAL
HOSTILES?
NEGATIVE

COMMENCE:
USER REVIVAL

ADMINISTER:
SMELLING SALTS

FSSSS

shump

shump

WUNNH!

WHERE...?

I DON'T BELIEVE IT! I *LIVE* IN LONG ISLAND, BUT I GOTTA COME ALL THE WAY TO THE *GREAT WALL O' CHINA* TO MEET *IRON MAN*!

MAURIE, TAKE OUR PICTURE!

WELCOME BACK TO CONSCIOUSNESS, TONE.

AS PER PRE-PROGRAMMED *PROTOCOLS,* ARMOR AUTOPILOT FLEW YOU TO THE NEAREST PUBLIC AREA.

WELL....I NEED YOU TO PLOT THE COORDINATES TO MANDARIN'S BASE FOR A *RETURN FLIGHT.*

EVEN IF MY WORKERS *HAVE* TURNED AGAINST ME, I CAN'T JUST LEAVE THEM IN *HIS* CLUTCHES--

RRUMBLL

WHOA! WHAT WAS *THAT?*

WAS IT *GOOD* OR *BAD?*

UM...

THANKS, PEPPER, FOR HELPING ME REALIZE I HAVE A **PROBLEM,** WHICH IS THE FIRST STEP TOWARD **SOLVING** IT--

WHATEVER! YOU AND TONY ARE TWO **PEAS** IN A POD...

MAN-CHILDREN!

YOU MAY HAVE SAVED **BEIJING,** BUT YOU'VE SEALED **YOUR** DOOM, IRON MAN!

I CAN STILL **OVERWHELM** YOU WITH **SHEER NUMBERS!**

UNUSUAL ENERGY SOURCE LOCATED

YOU DON'T **SAY...**

HORDES OF YOUR MASTER'S WORKERS-- UNARMED BUT FOR THEIR **HATRED** FOR YOU AND **STARK!**

THEY'LL JUST KEEP COMING **AT** YOU, OVER AND OVER, WAVE AFTER WAVE, IN SERVICE TO THEIR **KHAN,** UNTIL YOU AT LAST **FALL!**

ENERGY SOURCE DETERMINED TO BE--

RING: RIGHT RING FINGER

UNI-BEAM COHERENCY: NARROWEST SETTING

SPAK

WHAT...?

‹MY MIND--MY THOUGHTS--THEY'RE MINE AGAIN!›

‹WE'VE BEEN RELEASED FROM THE MANDARIN'S CONTROL SOMEHOW!›

‹STOP! STOP, MY SUBJECTS! IT IS BLASPHEMY TO DEFY YOUR KHAN!›

‹GRAB HIM--TAKE HIS RINGS-- MAKE SURE HE CAN'T HURT ANY MORE PEOPLE!›

‹WHAT A CROCK! I CAN'T BELIEVE HE MADE US SPOUT THAT "KHAN" NONSENSE!›

PLEASE CONVEY OUR APOLOGIES TO MR. STARK, IRON MAN.

WE HAD NO WISH TO LEAVE OUR POSTS AT HIS FACTORY, BUT OUR WILLS WERE ENSLAVED BY THE MANDARIN'S MIND-CONTROL RING.

UNDER THE CIRCUMSTANCES, I'M SURE MR. STARK WILL MORE THAN UNDERSTAND.

UGH! IT REEKS OF SWEAT IN THERE!

I HAVE NO IDEA HOW YOU CAN WEAR THIS SARDINE CAN ALL DAY.

IT'S AN ACQUIRED TASTE, I'LL ADMIT.

I APPRECIATE YOU PUTTING IT ON, HOW-EVER BRIEFLY. THAT SHOULD ALLAY ANY SUSPICIONS THAT TONY STARK AND IRON MAN ARE THE SAME GUY, NO?

BEFORE I FORGET--STARK INTERNATIONAL HUMAN RESOURCES PROTOCOL DICTATES THAT I, AS YOUR IMMEDIATE SUPERVISOR, PERSONALLY HAND YOU A COPY OF THIS.

Huh? WHAT'S--?

YOU'RE PUTTING A REPRIMAND IN MY EMPLOYEE FILE? WHY ARE YOU PUTTING A REPRIMAND IN MY EMPLOYEE FILE?

ACCORDING TO... UNNAMED SOURCES, YOU SPENT THE ENTIRE TIME I'VE BEEN HERE IN CHINA GOSSIPING LIKE A SCHOOL-GIRL ON THE PHONE...

...THAT IS, WHEN YOU WEREN'T PLAYING VIDEO GAMES.

"VIDEO--?" YOU KNOW I SPENT THAT WHOLE TIME SAVIN' YOUR BACON, TONE!

THIS IS ALL PEPPER'S DOING!

THAT MAY BE, BUT I, OF COURSE, CAN'T CLAIM TO HAVE ANY KNOWLEDGE OTHERWISE...

...WITHOUT JEOPARDIZING THAT PRECIOUS SECRET IDENTITY YOU'RE SO KEEN ON PROTECTING...

KNEW I NEVER SHOULDA LEFT THE SERVICE...

THE END

This footage from Pecos, Texas is the **first** proof that the monster does, in fact, exist.

The governor of Texas is suggesting that the surrounding towns **evacuate** and prepare for a possible **monster attack**.

CNND NEWS CHANNEL 10: SPECIAL REPORT

We will keep you updated with any **developments**. We now take you back to our regular scheduled programming.

Bruce Banner has been many things: scientist, inventor, gamma-irradiated monster... but one thing he's never been...

...I've never been to Texas!

...until now.

WELCOME TO TEXAS

THE LONE STAR STATE!
WHERE "FRIENDSHIP" COMES FIR

Okay everyone. I know we're a little *short* of our destination but this looks like the end of the road.

What? Why? I thought this went to Pecos, Texas.

It *did*.

And like I *said*...

This *is* the end of the road.

Are you okay, sir?

What--? Oh yeah. It's just so much destruction. I feel horrible.

You shouldn't feel bad, mister. It's not like *you* caused it.

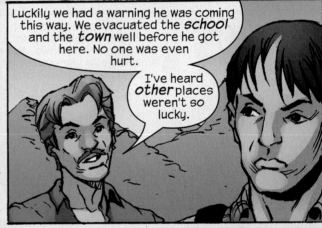

Luckily we had a warning he was coming this way. We evacuated the *school* and the *town* well before he got here. No one was even hurt.

I've heard *other* places weren't so lucky.

We were given the all-clear but the bridge is out, so here we sit.

So, everyone's okay. Good. Do they know where the--um-- *monster* went?

Not really, but you should check *this* out. He left a *calling card*.

Calling card?

We can't tell if this monster is a Bugs Bunny fan--or if this really *means* something.

No. It's no joke. Do you have any idea which direction the monster may have gone?

I can help you with *that*, too.

But I wouldn't suggest following those footprints. This thing is bad news. And a smaller fella like you is just gonna get himself hurt. No offense.

A two-mile walk later...

Hello? *Blonsky,* is it you down here?

I'm *honored* you remembered me, doc.

Hello, Emil. You're the only one who ever called me *"doc"* at The Project.

It's awful dark in here. Why don't we go outside and discuss this?

No thanks, *"doc".* I like the dark.

What did you *do* to yourself, Emil?

What do you *think* I did, Bruce?

I *continued* your *good work.*

But after my accident with the Gamma Radiation I destroyed *everything.* There was no record of it when I ran.

I remembered most of it. To a point. I tried to replicate the accident. Our boss seemed to think it was a good idea at the time.

The *Program* put you up to this?

No. I wanted to prove I could carry on without you. That *I* was just as good as *you* were.

And *did* you?

You tell me.

Oh, Emil... why did you come out here? Why were you looking for me?

Isn't it *obvious,* doc?

MARVEL CAPTAIN AMERICA

MARVEL FRANKLIN RICHARDS

MARVEL THOR

MARVEL INCREDIBLE HULK

MARVEL SPIDER-MAN

MARVEL IRON MAN

MARVEL SILVER SURFER

MARVEL POWER PACK

MARVEL STORM

MARVEL — THOR

The mighty Thor is the Asgardian God of thunder and lightning. With his magical hammer Mjolnir, Thor travels Earth protecting the planet and its inhabitants from all manners of magical beings and super-powered foes. Using his super-strength and ability to make lightning strike, Thor is a noble warrior who walks the Earth so others are safe to.

MARVEL — FRANKLIN RICHARDS

The young Franklin Richards is the smart and mischievous son of Mr. Fantastic and The Invisible Woman; members of the Fantastic Four. Franklin spends his days with his robot friend H.E.R.B.I.E. as they get into wild adventures with Franklin's father's futuristic inventions. When their escapades get out of control Franklin is able to use his common sense, ingenuity and intellect to fix the situation and save himself from being punished by his Super Hero parents.

MARVEL — CAPTAIN AMERICA

The star-spangled Avenger, Captain America, is a shining beacon of patriotism, skill, power and the American Spirit. Steve Rogers has physical abilities beyond the peak of a normal person and tactical skills that no computer can match. As leader of the Avengers and defender of all, Captain America is the hero that other heroes strive to be.

MARVEL — IRON MAN

Billionaire industrialist Tony Stark has the best toy in the world – a multi-million dollar suit of armor. And when he wears this amazing invention, the super-smart genius becomes the Invincible Iron Man, a crime fighting Super Hero whose powers are only limited by the extent of his intellect and imagination. With his red and gold armor full of technological gadgets and weapons like repulsor rays, energized gauntlets, and boot jets, Iron Man uses both his brains and his powers to stop any foe foolish enough to cross his path.

MARVEL — SPIDER-MAN

With great power comes great responsibility. Since the day that he was bitten by a radioactive spider, Peter Parker has had the proportionate abilities of an arachnid; super strength, lightning fast reflexes and agility, wall-crawling, and a "spider-sense" that warns him before danger strikes. Using his powers and wisecracking wit, the friendly neighborhood Spider-Man defends the streets of New York and all of its citizens from crime and mayhem.

MARVEL — INCREDIBLE HULK

Bruce Banner may appear to be your normal everyday scientist but within him lies…something else. When Bruce Banner, or those innocents around him, are in danger, the nerdy genius transforms into the giant, green, Gamma Radiation-powered Hulk. Using his huge muscles and incredible strength, the immensely powerful hero defends those too weak to protect themselves.

MARVEL — STORM

The mutant Ororo Munroe, also known as Storm, has command over the forces of the weather and nature. Storm uses her powers as leader of the X-Men to protect mutants that are feared and hated. Like the weather itself, Storm's capabilities range from a gentle summer breeze to a powerful hurricane. She keeps her powers and emotions in check by focusing on a better tomorrow and future for mutants and humans alike.

MARVEL — POWER PACK

Power Pack consists of four super powered siblings. Alex Power is able to manipulate gravity while Julie can fly on a rainbow stream. Jack Power turns into a cloud by controlling his density and Katie Power manipulates energy for her own heroic purposes. Calling themselves Power Pack, these super powered brothers and sisters travel together righting wrongs and getting into all kinds of crazy adventures.

MARVEL — SILVER SURFER

The high-flying Silver Surfer is infused with cosmic energy. Once the herald of the planet-eating Galactus, the Surfer has made Earth his new home planet as he travels the cosmos on his amazing surfboard, protecting beings from forces seeking to upset the cosmic balance. His powers are only matched by his will to protect all sentient life in the universe.

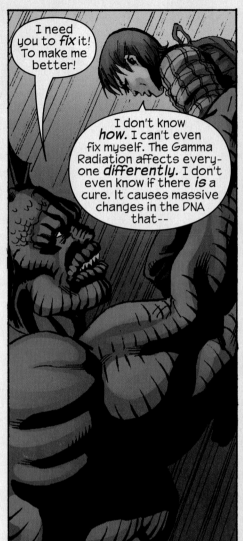

I need you to *fix* it! To make me better!

I don't know *how*. I can't even fix myself. The Gamma Radiation affects everyone *differently*. I don't even know if there *is* a cure. It causes massive changes in the DNA that--

Then how come you're in normal form now? Why can't I change back and forth?

I don't really change back and forth on a *whim*. Our exposure levels were completely different so there's no way to--

Liar!

Please, Emil. Calm down. We both need to stay calm.

I'm an *abomination!* A *monster!* Why can't I change back?

I don't know. But you have to stop acting crazy. You're a good man, Emil, but destroying cities-- endangering lives. This isn't you.

It is *now.*

Where are you going?

Back to pay the town of *Orlon* another visit. The folks were all out of town on my last tour. It kind of took the fun out of it.

You can't!

Why not? I'm a monster. At least until you figure out a cure.

Maybe some time alone down here will help you *focus* a little.

RRRIIIIPPP!

NO! Hurting people-- destroying things isn't the answer!

Emil! Blonsky! My leg--

You still have your mind! We could work on a cure *together!* Please come back! Blonsky! Please! The Gamma Radiation affects people's psyches differently.

It split my personality in two. Whenever I'm stressed the Hulk comes out. The Emil Blonsky I knew wasn't *ethical* but he didn't want to hurt *innocent people.*

No! Don't hurt *people* with my discoveries!

I need yo-- *aaahhhhh!*

AHHHHH!

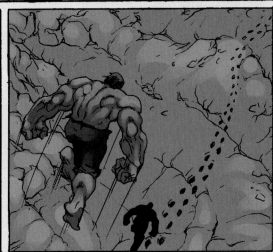

Uhh.

I'm not done yet. I can't believe I was trying to follow in your footsteps. I didn't realize that you only turned green and moronic.

Don't you have any special powers? Maybe you can fly...

I guess not.

THUD!

I can't believe this is *it*, Hulk. This is *all* you've got?

Don't give up yet, Bruce.

I want to see what this body can do. And *you're* the only thing around I can really cut loose on.

Perfect. I was hoping you had some fight left. Because I wanted to share a *hypothesis* with you.

Something has become obvious to me. My version of the experiment was a *success*. I succeeded where you failed, Banner.

I've created the ultimate weapon--*me*.

You're going to be a footnote in history, Hulk. Weak.

Just like your alter ego, Dr. Bruce Banner.

Can't you see you're nothing compared to me?

SLAM!

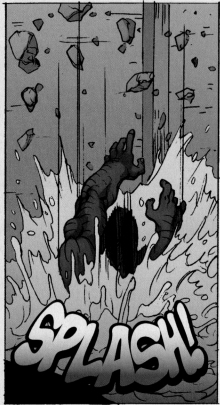

SPLASH!

Lucky shot.

...but that's the last free ride you get.

SMASH!

I was taking it easy on you because we have a history, doc...

You're coming with me back to The Program!

SPLASH!

The old gang will convince you to give up all your Gamma secrets. They have their ways, doc!

And then you're going to find a cure for my condit--

Big monster talk too much!

Wha--?

NO!

Later...

We've recovered Blonsky, sir.

No, sir. No sign of Banner.

Except for the beating he put on Blonsky.

Nothing, sir. We're placing Blonsky in the *containment* tank now and we'll have him home in no time.

"Banner couldn't have gotten far, sir."

YOU ARE NOW LEAVING

TEXAS,
THE LONE STAR STATE.

DON'T FORGET ABOUT YOUR FRIENDS IN TEX

"We'll find him. It's only a matter of time."

WELCOME TO OKLAHOMA

End.

SPIDER-MAN SNAPSHOT

Use the grid below to complete the picture of Spidey!

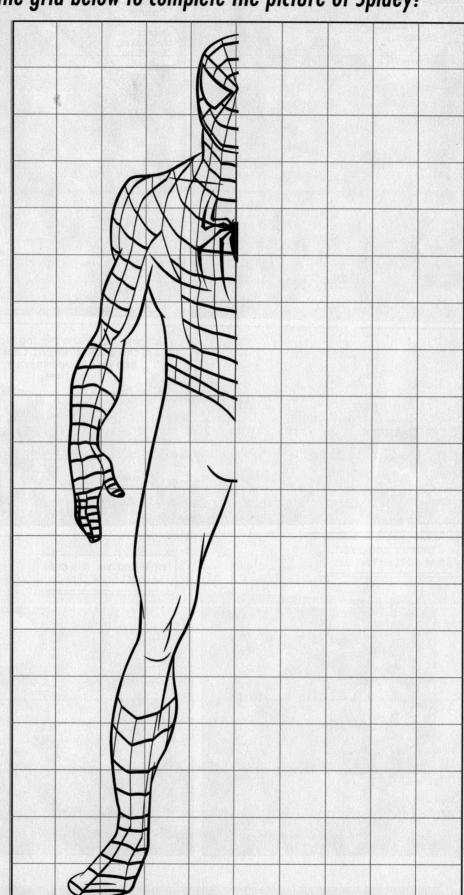